Long ago, in the

Zeus and Hera

...grotesque inanimate idols as their neighbors did. They worshipped, instead, an extended family of radiant, omnipotent beings. In this beautiful mythological world, the sun, moon, and stars were gods and goddesses whose shape-shifting powers allowed them to descend to Earth undetected. Though the Greek myths were conceived over four thousand years ago, the inventive and often humorous exploits of their protagonists continue to delight readers to this day.

Perhaps one reason Greek myths continue to be relatable and entertaining is that, unlike myths of other early cultures, the ancient Greeks worshipped deities who were heroic versions of themselves yet subject to all the best and worst impulses of human nature. Depending on his mood, the mercurial Zeus could be magnanimous or vengeful. One day, he bestows the gift of immortality on a mortal woman so that Eros can marry her; on another, in a colossal overreaction, Zeus ties Prometheus to a rock, for all time, for not consulting him before empowering mankind with fire. It is apparent that the most powerful god in the pantheon suffers from a very fragile ego!

Prometheus

In Greek mythology, the gods, no matter how powerful, are often confronted with some of the very same issues that challenge their human counterparts. Even Helios, the mighty god of the sun, has trouble standing up to his headstrong son, Phaethon, when he demands the reins to Helios's chariot.

The earliest myths were man's first attempt at explaining nature's mysteries. As farmers and seafarers, the ancient Greeks were hugely affected by changes in the seasons and swiftly shifting weather patterns. How did they make sense of these seemingly random forces? They created a whole world populated with superhuman beings, each with his or her own sphere of influence; and each of whom wielded power according to his or her whim. Who but an angry god would disturb the peace with a thunderbolt? And that rainbow after the storm?—surely the work of a benevolent goddess come to paint the sky as a sign that all was right with the world.

Iris

Demeter

It is no wonder that Zeus, the bringer of rain, would be awarded the most important rank in the pantheon. Rainfall was critical to the inhospitable rocky soil of Greece. Without it, Demeter could not bless the harvest, and Bacchus would be without grapes to make his wine. But why would the land harden with frost so that not even the hardiest plant might survive until spring? Could it be that Demeter, goddess of the harvest, had withdrawn her blessings from the Earth because she had gone into mourning? The metaphor is both creative and profound, for who would not identify with a grieving mother?

The beauty and wonder of the world could be as baffling as its harsher realities. An echo heard within a cave must have startled and then delighted the first mythmakers, giving rise to the story of Echo and Narcissus. How to explain the incomparable radiance of a peacock's feathers? The early Greeks did not have an app for that but they did have a myth!

Hermes and Pandora

Another reason for the enduring power of the myths may lie in the universality of their themes. Though modern man has become technologically advanced, human nature seems not to have progressed much at all. The ills released by Pandora are certainly still with us today. Leave it to the ancient poets to put greed in its proper perspective. The story of King Midas, for whom no amount of wealth was ever enough, demonstrates in a most concrete way the effects that greed can have over more worthy human values.

Judging by the popularity of the tabloids, people are still just as fascinated by rumors of infidelity as the ancient Greeks once were, with tales of Zeus and Hera. We can also be sure that the vain Narcissus had nothing on certain political figures who populate the news today. Though psychology may explain what makes us tick, most would agree that the myths are far more entertaining.

Narcissus

Few can resist the power of a good love story and Greek mythology fairly vibrates with romantic intrigue. The stories of Eros and Psyche, Hades and Persephone, Ceyx and Alcyon, and Orpheus and Eurydice have inspired the world's great masterpieces, from opera to painting to literature.

Orpheus

Greek myths continue to permeate our culture. A maker of designer handbags is named for Hermes, the god who kept a leather pouch by his side. A company that provides a wide range of music to its subscribers is aptly named for Pandora, whose name means "all gifts" in Greek. Our word "cereal" derives from Ceres, goddess of the harvest, and the word "arachnophobia" can be traced to the arrogant Arachne. Names for our planets (Uranus and Saturn) and constellations, such as Hercules and Pleiades to name a few, as well as the words "atlas" and "echo," are all rooted in mythology.

The earliest Greek myths were passed down orally from generation to generation. Honed and embellished with each telling, by the time they were written down, every story was suffused with a collective flare. The myths' poignancy derives from the ancient poets' genius for writing stories that transformed an often treacherous world into one of transcendent beauty.

Arachne

The Trojan War was fought over the beautiful, mortal Helen of Troy. In a passage from the ancient Greek poet Euripides, Helen laments, "If only I could shed my beauty and assume an uglier aspect, the way you would wipe color off a statue."

Science has confirmed what classical literature has hinted at: that ancient Greek architecture as well as its statuary were far from colorless. Though invisible to the naked eye, ultraviolet light has revealed that they had been painted with pigments rendered from crushed plants, stones, and shells. Color may fade over time, but the composition of these organic materials has not changed, so we can deduce exactly how the original works of art might have appeared to ancient eyes.

For Euripides, it was understood that wiping color off a statue would diminish its beauty because in his classical Greek culture, beauty and color were inextricably linked. It might help to keep this in mind as you color the scenes of these ancient tales, restoring them once more to their original splendor.

GREEK MYTHOLOGY
A COLORING BOOK

MARY PAPPAS PACKARD
ILLUSTRATIONS BY CHELLIE CARROLL

METRO BOOKS
New York

On Mt. Olympus

Far above Earth's highest peaks, a pantheon of deities once made their home in a mysterious realm called Mt. Olympus. These immortals governed Earth and made rules for the mortals who worshipped them—though the gods' own moral code was far more flexible. Capable of performing wondrous feats at will, they enjoyed flaunting them to each other, as well as to the earthlings below. Sometimes the Olympians would visit Earth undisguised; at other times, they descended in animal or human forms. No rain or snow ever fell on their celestial paradise, nor did the wind ever disturb its tranquility.

THE OLYMPIAN TWELVE

Twelve deities dwelled on Mt. Olympus. The most powerful were the siblings Zeus, Hera, Poseidon, and Demeter. Their king, Zeus, god of the skies, settled their disputes and punished their transgressions. The formidable Hera was his wife and queen. The guardian of marriage and childbirth, Hera kept a close watch on her two-timing husband.

Poseidon, god of the sea, was second in command. With one stroke of his trident, the mighty Poseidon created earthquakes on land and shipwrecks at sea. Demeter, goddess of the harvest, lavished her attentions on Earth so that its people would flourish.

THE CHILDREN OF ZEUS

Hermes, the messenger god, served as the liaison between the gods and humans, as he accompanied the dead on their journey to the underworld. Clever and devious, he was also known as the god of trickery. Athena, the goddess of wisdom, was the favorite child of Zeus, having leapt from his head fully grown! She was also the goddess of war and the domestic arts, and as such, her guidance was sought by soldiers and housewives alike.

Apollo was the god of light, truth, and the healing arts. This extraordinarily gifted fellow was often heard serenading his fellow Olympians with tunes on his golden lyre. Artemis, Apollo's twin sister, was goddess of the hunt, the moon, and chastity.

Dionysus, the god of wine and the grape harvest, held the distinction of being the only Olympian born of a mortal mother. The kind and gentle Hephaestus, god of fire, excelled at metalworking and sculpture. His wife, Aphrodite, goddess of love and beauty, was said to have sprung from the foam of the sea.

Ares was the god of war. His domain, unlike Athena's, which dealt with strategy, was associated with bloodshed and brutality. The least favored of Zeus's children, he was one of the few offspring whom Zeus conceived with his wife, Hera.

IN THE BEGINNING . . .

The ancestors of the Olympian gods were the Titans. Before the Titans, there had been only chaos, a formless void of swirling darkness. Not until Earth (called Gaea then), made her appearance, did the world as we know it take shape. No one knows how or from where Gaea sprang. All that is known is that Gaea, the giver of all life, was exceedingly lonely before the first beings lived upon her. One day, Gaea looked up and saw Sky (called Uranus then) and fell hopelessly in love. Uranus smiled down at Gaea with a multitude of twinkling stars.

Uranus and Gaea were joined in love, and from their union sprang the Titans. The leader of the Titans was Cronus, father of Zeus. When Zeus grew up, he led his siblings in a successful revolt against Cronus who was a cruel father and ruthless leader.

As the new ruler of the universe, Zeus made it his business to fulfill his mother's dearest wish: to cover the Earth with living beings. He awarded the job of creating a kingdom of animals to Epimetheus, a Titan who had remained loyal to him during the war against Cronus. Epimetheus endowed his creatures with myriad gifts, protecting their bodies with scales, feathers, fur, and shells. He also supplied some with wings and fins for speed and others with sharp claws and teeth to defend themselves.

Zeus conferred the honor of creating the first man on Prometheus, who carefully and lovingly shaped his new being out of mud. Since Epimetheus had already given all the best qualities to the animals, Prometheus decided to let man stand upright and walk on two feet as the gods themselves did. When he was satisfied with his sculpture, he asked Athena to breathe life into it. Prometheus fashioned more of these creatures, whom he called "man."

When Prometheus saw that they were cold at night without the sun's rays to warm them, and unable to see when the moon's light was dim, he stole some fire from Hephaestus and gave it to man. Outraged that he had not been consulted, Zeus punished Prometheus by having him chained to a high cliff where he would forever be exposed to the elements.

Pandora's Box

To punish man for receiving the gift of fire, Zeus decided to create a new human of stunning beauty, one that men would be unable to resist. He called the new creature "woman," and named her Pandora. He then asked each of his fellow Olympians to donate something of value to her. Athena clothed Pandora in splendid garments that she wove herself. Aphrodite gave her beauty and Apollo, music. Demeter bestowed Pandora a "green thumb" so that she would always have flowers to delight her, while Poseidon taught the new woman how to swim so that she would never drown. Hephaestus adorned her with fabulous jewels of his own creation.

Hermes gave Pandora a pretty box that Zeus ordered her never to open. Last but definitely not least, Hera endowed her with curiosity.

Finally, the Olympians delivered Pandora to Epimetheus, who accepted her gladly. All would have been well had Pandora not come with that box. She wished to obey the gods with all her heart—all except for that little part that just had to know what lay inside Hermes's present. She opened the box just a crack and out flew sorrow, jealousy, hate, and greed. Luckily, there was one good thing among all those miseries: it was called hope. Hope had been placed there as a consolation for all of those ills that have plagued mankind ever since.

A CRUSHING FATE

None of Cronus's Titans was punished more harshly than Atlas, who was forced to bear the weight of the world on his shoulders. His daughters, the seven Pleiades, adored their father, and it pained them beyond measure to see him struggle to keep from being crushed by his burden. In the end, they took their own lives so they would no longer have to watch their father suffer.

With great remorse, Zeus turned the sisters' bodies into stars—the constellation known as the Pleiades, or Seven Sisters—to insure that they would never be forgotten.

HERA AND THE PEACOCK

Though Zeus had a beautiful wife, Hera, he had no intention of forsaking others. Far from it! Zeus loved Hera, but he also loved Greece, and so he took it upon himself to populate the land with his superior offspring. Unfortunately, for Zeus, Hera was as clever as she was beautiful. Though she loved her husband, she was onto him. One day, a storm cloud darkened a sky that had just seconds before been clear and bright with sunshine. Suspecting that Zeus was up to his old tricks, Hera swooped down to Earth to investigate.

Zeus heard the unmistakable swish of Hera's robes as she descended. He had been enjoying the charms of a beautiful young maiden named Io and had created the cloud to conceal their tryst. Eager to escape his wife's wrath, he cast a spell on Io, and in an instant, the beautiful maiden was transformed into a lovely white heifer.

Hera was not fooled; she knew that her husband had not been cavorting with a cow! So she asked Zeus to present her with the cow as a gift. How could Zeus refuse? And so as not to tip his hand, he gave in to his wife's demand. Hera tied the cow to an olive tree, and then sent for her servant, Argus, to watch over her day and night.

Zeus ached to free Io, but who could slip by Argus, the giant endowed with one hundred eyes?

Perhaps Hermes, the god of trickery, might know what to do, thought Zeus. So he called upon his son for help. Hermes disguised himself as a shepherd, and when he was in earshot of Argus, he began to play a sleepy tune. One by one, the giant's eyes began to droop as Hermes patiently lulled Argus to sleep with his enchanted flute. When all hundred eyes had closed, Hermes seized his chance. He slayed the fierce giant and set Io free.

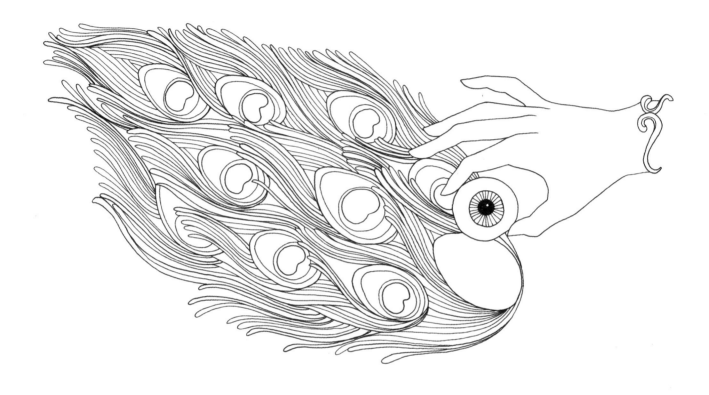

Hera was devastated to find that her faithful servant had met such a cruel end. To honor his memory, Hera carefully removed the eyes from Argus's dead body and set them into the plumage of her favorite bird, the peacock.

ECHO AND NARCISSUS

When Hera suspected that Zeus had begun an affair with a woodland nymph, she visited Earth to find out who had claimed his affections. Upon landing, she was immediately distracted by the incessant chatter of the beautiful Echo, who was known for her long-winded, yet extremely entertaining stories. While Echo prattled away, Zeus and his lover made a hasty exit. Enraged, Hera took out her anger on Echo by stripping her of her ability to form her own words. From that day on, Echo was capable only of repeating the words of others.

Poor Echo! She had been deprived of her most engaging talent. Even worse, she would never be able to use that talent to seduce the love of her life. This young man, whose name was Narcissus, was so handsome that no woman could resist him.

Narcissus had no interest in the fair maidens who adored him because he was just as in love with himself as they were. One day, as Echo watched from the shadows, she spied Narcissus at the water's edge.

Narcissus knelt down to take a drink and caught sight of his own reflection in the spring. Why, it was the handsomest face he had ever seen! Spellbound, he could not tear his eyes from the shimmering image, and so he remained at the water's edge, forgetting to eat or drink, gradually wasting away until there was nothing left of him. In his place, there grew a gorgeous plant, the Narcissus flower, that was named for him. Grief stricken, Echo remained at the water's edge, pining for Narcissus until she, too, faded away. All that remained of her was her voice, which to this day can be heard randomly repeating the words of others

ARACHNE GOES TOO FAR

The goddess Athena was known for skills at the loom that were unsurpassed. Since she was always happy to share her weaving techniques, she had many pupils. One of her students, a simple country girl named Arachne, outshone all the others.

No one was more impressed with her own work than Arachne, who took to boasting that her weaving was even better than her teacher's. Greatly offended, Athena transformed herself into an old lady and then flew down to Earth to warn Arachne to be more respectful of the gods.

"Why not let the goddess Athena bring her best work and compare it to mine?" challenged Arachne.

Just then, Athena threw off her disguise and proceeded to create a most splendid tapestry, a glorious depiction of the Olympians, woven in silk and shot through with threads of gold and silver. Arachne's tapestry was also flawlessly woven, but its subject was a mocking portrayal of Zeus with his lovers.

"How dare you ridicule the ruler of the gods?" exclaimed Athena. Upon saying this, she sprinkled Arachne with a potion that turned the boastful girl into a lowly spider.

"You will continue to weave, my dear," she spat, "but now you will do your weaving in the air."

POSEIDON AND DEMETER

Poseidon divided his time between Mt. Olympus and the underwater palace that he shared with his wife, Amphitrite. Artfully created out of coral and shiny seashells, the magnificent palace was surrounded by colorful gardens where sea nymphs called Nereids frolicked among the water lilies. Inside, the floors sparkled with pearls and the walls shone with embedded gems.

One day, the sea god's roving eye fell on Demeter. Demeter was not interested in having an affair with Poseidon, so to divert him, she challenged Poseidon to create the most wondrous animal the world had ever seen.

Not one to shrink from a challenge, Poseidon labored obsessively until he had produced a magnificent steed. The beast stood tall on slender legs built for speed, and its majestic neck was graced with a silken mane of flowing tresses.

Poseidon produced several more of these brand-new creatures that he called "horses." He then put them to good use, harnessing them to a chariot that sped him across the surface of the sea. To herald his arrival, green-eyed sea creatures called Tritons emerged from the waves blowing on trumpets made of shells. They were joined by playful dolphins and Nereids who also surfaced at Poseidon's approach.

Poseidon became so enthralled with his creations that he lost all interest in pursuing Demeter. Her ploy had worked and no one could have felt more relieved!

PHAETHON AND THE CHARIOT

As he matured, young Phaethon, son of the Titan Helios, god of the sun, began to doubt that he had such an illustrious father. His classmates didn't believe the story, either, making fun of him whenever he mentioned it.

Every day after school, Phaethon would beg his mother, the sea nymph Clymene, to send him to visit his father in the heavens so that he could find out for sure. And each day, Clymene would deny his request, believing the trip too long and arduous for one so young. With each passing day, Phaethon became more persistent, until at last, Clymene relented and sent him on his way.

Phaethon shielded his eyes as he stepped into the throne room of the mighty Helios, who wore a crown of blinding light and robes that glittered with jewels.

"Why are you here?" asked the sun god.
"I have come to ask if you are my father," declared Phaethon.
"I am," Helios replied, kindly. "And I will prove it to you. Ask for anything and I will grant it."
"I wish to drive your chariot."
"Oh no!" exclaimed Helios in alarm. "The trip is far too perilous. Ask for anything but that!"

But Phaethon could not be dissuaded. He persisted and cajoled, until finally, Helios gave in to the headstrong boy.

Phaethon could not believe that he would soon be driving the sun across the sky! At first, he stood proudly in his father's chariot, thrilled with the importance of his task. However, it soon became apparent that he lacked the strength to hold the horses in check, and it wasn't long before he lost all control!

The horses had veered off course, flying much too high and creating a large gash in the sky that is known as the Milky Way. Next, the horses flew too low, scorching the Earth with the sun's heat. When Zeus saw that even the life-giving rainclouds had retreated in fear, he threw a thunderbolt in the chariot's path, causing the inept Phaethon to plunge to his death into the river below. Hephaestus labored all evening to repair the chariot so that Helios, through his tears, might fulfill his duty and bring sunlight to Earth by morning.

DEMETER AND PERSEPHONE

Demeter was a goddess who was loved by all. She brought fertility to the soil to make it bountiful with life-giving harvests. As if that were not enough, to delight the senses, she blanketed the earth with colorful wildflowers, perfuming the air with their fragrance. Demeter asked for nothing in return, only to bask in the company of her beautiful daughter, Persephone, whom she prized above all things.

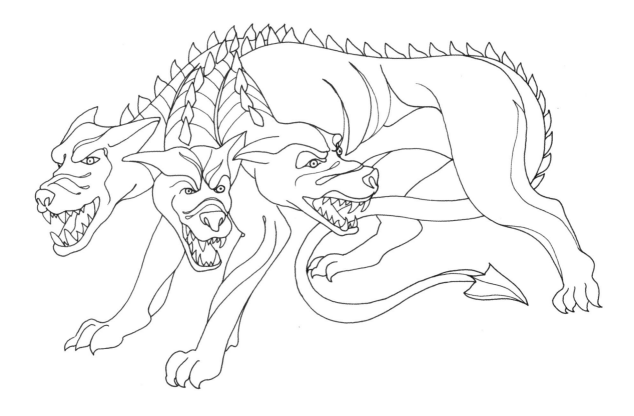

One day Hades left the underworld to take his three-headed dog, Cerberus, for a romp in a meadow. There, he spied the lovely Persephone, who was picking violets to give to her mother. *How beautiful she is!* thought Hades. And when he saw the young girl fearlessly greet his bizarre beast with affection, he fell instantly in love with her. Scooping Persephone into his chariot, Hades sped her away to his underworld realm.

Hades led the weeping Persephone to the most sumptuous room in his palace. He proffered her splendid clothes and sparkling gems, but Persephone refused them all. She even refused to eat, having heard that once anything was consumed in the underworld, one could never leave.

Demeter searched far and wide for her daughter. Her grief was so great that she delivered a solemn oath to the gods: if she did not succeed in finding Persephone, never again would she adorn the Earth with flowers or provide a full harvest of vegetables, fruits, and grains to feed its people.

Aware that the world would perish without Demeter's care, Zeus sent Hermes to rescue Persephone. Hermes hastened to the underworld, but he arrived too late.

Poor Persephone! After starving herself for weeks, she could no longer deny herself. *Perhaps a tiny snack wouldn't count*, she reasoned, and with that, she popped six pomegranate seeds into her mouth. Hades was so overjoyed that when Hermes arrived, he welcomed him with a smile.

"I would like to help you, my boy," he said, "but there is just one problem." As he pointed to the bowl of half-eaten pomegranate seeds, Hades said, "Perhaps we can strike a compromise."

Unwilling to risk an all-out war with the other gods and goddesses, Hades agreed to share Persephone with her mother: the six months that Persephone spent with Hades—one month for each pomegranate seed she had eaten—the cold of winter would chill the Earth; when she returned to her mother, spring and summer would travel with her.

KING MIDAS AND THE GOLDEN TOUCH

The god Dionysus was never without his beloved companion, a satyr named Silenus.

Once, after a night of revelry, Silenus wandered off in a drunken stupor. It was several days before the jovial, old satyr was discovered passed out in the garden of a pleasure-loving king named Midas. Midas returned Silenus to Dionysus, who was so grateful that he promised to grant the king his dearest wish.

"No one can have enough wealth," declared Midas. "Do you think you could make everything I touch turn to gold?"

"So be it!" granted Dionysus with a flourish, and it wasn't long before the objects in the king's palace began to sparkle at his touch—columns, staircases, banisters, doors, floors . . . !

But the king soon discovered that not everything was improved with gold. As Midas strolled through his garden, he found that his roses had lost their fragrance, and when food or drink touched his lips, it became impossible to swallow. Then, before he could warn her, the king's child leapt into his arms, and right before his eyes, she became a cold, lifeless statue.

A sobbing Midas begged Dionysus to take back the spell.

"Bathe in the Pactolus river," replied the god. King Midas did as he was told and the spell was broken. All returned to normal—that is, all but the river, which has water that remains golden to this day.

THE NINE MUSES

After spending nine days and nights with Zeus, Mnemosyne, the goddess of memory, produced nine beautiful and talented daughters known to the Olympians as the nine muses. Mnemosyne's memory was as long as the beautiful hair that fell below her waist. She regaled her daughters with stories about the creation of the Earth, sun, and stars, and about the wonderful exploits of their father, Zeus. Apollo trained the muses to sing in nine-part harmony and led them through the halls of Olympus, where the gods and goddesses rejoiced at what they heard. When the muses sang on Earth, the people would forget all of their sorrows—such was the gift that they gave freely to the world.

ORPHEUS AND EURYDICE

In time, each muse became known for her expertise in one subject. The beautiful Calliope excelled at poetry. So lovely were her verses that the King of Thrace fell in love with her even before he set eyes on her. Calliope returned his love, and before long, their union was blessed with the birth of a son, whom they named Orpheus.

This boy was gifted with a voice so pure that upon hearing its dulcet tones, even warriors would lay down their swords. Birds ceased their singing, fierce beasts swallowed their roars, and rocks rolled toward the sound, so compelling was its timbre. It is not surprising then that the young man had little trouble gaining the affection of the lovely Eurydice, with whom he fell in love at first sight.

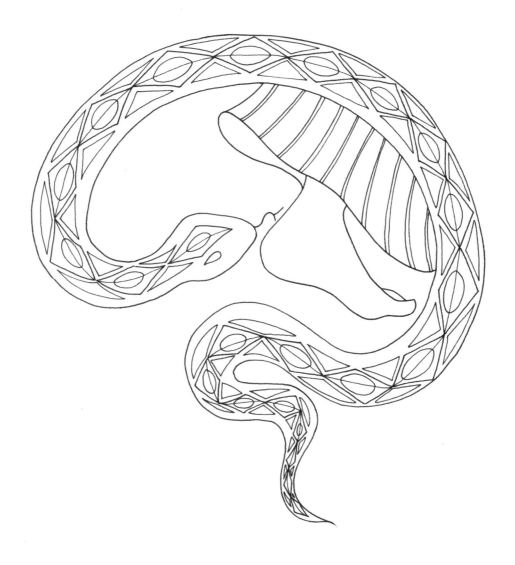

Eurydice agreed to marry Orpheus, but on the day of the wedding, she was mortally bitten by a snake. Hermes gently closed her eyes and carried her to Hades. Stricken with grief, Orpheus wandered the Earth looking for the entrance to the underworld. He found it at last, and with hope in his heart, he began the long, terrifying descent.

If my voice has the power to move boulders, he reasoned, *perhaps Hades will be moved by my music as well.*

As Orpheus sang his way through the dark passage, all movement ceased.

Suddenly, the iron gates parted and there stood Eurydice, a vibrant vision among the souls of the dead.

Hades was so moved by the heartbreaking music that he agreed to let Eurydice leave on one condition: Orpheus must not look back at his bride on his ascent from the underworld. Orpheus led Eurydice through the long, winding labyrinth, but at the last moment, he was gripped by doubt.

Perhaps Hades has tricked me, he thought, turning to make sure that Eurydice was still behind him. In an instant, Hermes appeared at her side to carry her back to the underworld.

"Farewell," whispered Eurydice, and she was whisked from his sight forever.

ALCYONE AND CEYX

The son of the Morning Star, King Ceyx, and his wife, Queen Alcyone, the daughter of Aeolus, keeper of the wind, ruled their kingdom with wisdom and compassion. The couple was admired as much for their devotion to one another as for their physical beauty. At times, they would refer to each other as "Zeus and Hera," a joke they shared privately between them. But the gods hear all things, and Zeus was not pleased with their arrogance.

"How dare those two compare themselves to gods!" he thundered.

Zeus had been waiting for the perfect moment to humiliate the king. When it was time for Ceyx to make the long sea voyage to consult the oracle at Delphi, he seized his chance.

"Let us see how you measure up to the gods tonight!" cried Zeus, hurling his thunderbolt at the king's ship and splitting the boat in two. As he lay dying, Ceyx called out Alcyone's name. Water soon filled his lungs, however, and stopped the beating of his heart.

The next day, the Morning Star refused to shine.

Meanwhile, Alcyone was counting the days until her husband's return. She passed the time at her loom, weaving a luxurious robe for Ceyx as a welcome-home present.

Hera's heart ached for the young widow, so she sent for her personal messenger, Iris, the goddess of the rainbow, and instructed: "Tell Morpheus to send Alcyone a dream so she will know that her husband has died."

Hovering over Alcyone's sleeping form, Morpheus created a lifelike specter of Ceyx that revealed all that had befallen him. In her grief, Alcyone ran to the seashore screaming his name. There, she saw the body of her husband that had washed ashore.

Determined to join Ceyx in death, Alcyone threw herself into the sea.

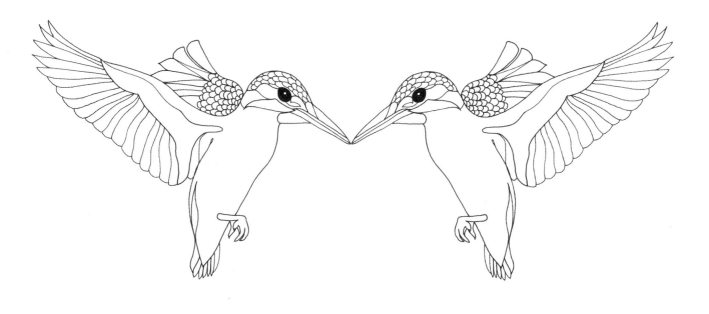

All of a sudden, instead of drowning, Alcyone found herself beating the water with powerful wings. Her body grew feathers and her mouth, a beak, as she rose above the water. She touched Ceyx's lips with her beak and he, too, began to rise with her. Saddened by the lovers' tragic fate, the gods on Olympus did what they could, changing the couple into halcyons (or kingfishers) so that they could be together forever.

Ever since that day, Aeolus keeps the wind to himself for seven days and nights, stilling the ocean so that Alcyone can brood her sandy nest, undisturbed by crashing waves. Today, we often refer to times of peace and contentment as "halcyon days" in memory of this couple's steadfast love.

PSYCHE AND EROS

Long ago, a king and queen had three daughters. All three were lovely, but the one named Psyche outshone the others. She was so stunning that people began to whisper that she was a goddess. Suitors came from far and wide to ask for her hand in marriage. In lieu of attending festivals to honor Aphrodite, the people honored Psyche instead, throwing rose petals in her path as she went about the kingdom.

Outraged that she was being displaced by a mere mortal, Aphrodite ordered her son, Eros (or Cupid), the god of love, to use his arrow to make Psyche fall in love with the most repulsive creature he could find. Eros flew off to do his mother's bidding, but alas, he, too, fell in love with Psyche.

Psyche had no wish to marry a man who saw only her physical beauty but not the soul within. Perplexed by his daughter's refusal to marry, the king consulted the oracle at Delphi. The oracle delivered a harsh message from the gods:

"The king must lead Psyche to the top of a mountain to await her future husband, a winged serpent."

The heartbroken king left Psyche weeping and trembling to await her fate. But instead of a winged serpent, the gentle West Wind swept Psyche off to a beautiful valley and set her down beside a treasure-filled palace. "All this belongs to you," crooned the voices of invisible beings. Their sweet music lured Psyche into the palace, where she was treated to a magnificent feast.

That night, as Psyche lay in her bed, she felt someone lie down beside her. A kind voice told her that the gods had decreed that though he was her husband, he must forever be invisible to her. She should not worry, he assured her, because he would always keep her safe. Swayed by his gentle demeanor, Psyche accepted her fate and allowed the presence to make love to her. He left before daybreak while she slept.

In time, Eros arranged for the West Wind to whisk Psyche's sisters to their home in the clouds for a visit. At first, they were delighted to find Psyche alive and well, but when they saw her gleaming palace and all of her treasures, they became jealous.

"Perhaps your lover is a serpent who transforms himself at will," they suggested. "No riches are worth having a monster for a husband."

The sisters told Psyche to place a lamp near the bed so that after her husband falls asleep, she can sneak a peek at him. At first she resisted the idea, but her curiosity got the better of her. In the lamplight, Psyche was astounded to see that, far from being a monster, her husband was a handsome god with golden curls and chiseled features. Examining an arrow from his golden quiver, she accidently pricked her finger and was immediately suffused with a love so great that it knew no bounds. She was so distracted that she accidently tilted the lamp. A drop of the oil spilled onto Eros's shoulder, startling him awake.

"If only you had trusted me," Eros lamented. "Now I have no choice but to leave you forever."

Eros carried Psyche down from the heavens. On their way, he revealed all that had led to this sad day—how he had disobeyed his mother's orders and unleashed the power of her wrath. Now that Psyche had disobeyed the gods, too, Aphrodite would surely have her revenge.

And so the lovers were forced to part. With each passing day, Eros became more despondent, until at last, he retreated to Mt. Olympus. Without Eros in attendance, the world became a desolate place. Lovers no longer cared for each other, parents neglected their children, and affection withered and died among friends. Filled with remorse, Psyche decided to visit Aphrodite and beg for permission to visit her son.

Aphrodite led Psyche to a storeroom where assorted grains were mingled in a towering heap. "Sort these by nightfall," she commanded. "Only after then will I consider your request."

Psyche would have done anything for a chance to see Eros again, and so she set about sorting the grain. Just then, an army of ants appeared and climbed the heap. Carrying one grain at a time, they worked until each grain was in its proper pile.

"Who helped you?" Aphrodite shrieked, when she saw that the task had been completed to perfection. "No matter," she added, "there is no shortage of tasks that await you."

Next, Aphrodite sent Psyche to gather golden wool from the fierce rams that grazed by the river.

Once again, the lovesick Psyche was willing to try. Before she could get close to the dangerous beasts, a river god whispered in her ear: "Do not sacrifice yourself, Psyche. Wait for the beasts to fall asleep and then gather the wool they've left on the sharp briar bushes."

Of course, the sight of the gathered golden wool did nothing to appease the vengeful goddess, who sent the intrepid Psyche on another, even more dangerous mission.

"Ask Persephone to fill this this box with a bit of her beauty," Aphrodite ordered.

Psyche was all too aware that for a mortal, death was the only path to the underworld. She was about to hasten her journey by taking her own life, when once again, a voice intervened: "Do not harm yourself," it advised. "Take one coin and two pieces of barley cake with you to the River Styx. The coin is for Charon, who will ferry you to the underworld, and the barley cake will tame Cerberus, the three-headed dog. Remember, once Persephone has filled the box, do not open it."

Psyche did as she was told . . . well almost. Flushed with success but feeling worn out from the effort, she decided to borrow a bit of Persephone's beauty from the box. Alas, out flew not beauty but a powerful potion that sent the young woman into a deep sleep.

Meanwhile, Eros, who had regained his strength, was searching for Psyche. At length, he spied her on the ground and flew down to her crumpled form. He removed the sleep from her eyes and placed it back in the box. Then waking Psyche with a kiss, he flew off with her to Mt. Olympus to beg for the gods' help.

Zeus, who was in a glorious mood that day, gathered all the gods and goddesses to witness a rare and solemn rite. To the celestial strains of Apollo's lyre, they all watched as Psyche took a taste of ambrosia—the powerful elixir that would make her a goddess by conferring everlasting life. It was a joyous occasion! It wouldn't be long before Eros and Pysche, who were now free to live as husband and wife, would welcome a baby daughter. They named her Bliss.

METRO BOOKS
New York

An Imprint of Sterling Publishing Co., Inc.
1166 Avenue of the Americas
New York, NY 10036

ISBN – 978-1-4351-6376-8

Distributed in Canada by Sterling Publishing
c/o Canadian Manda Group, 165 Dufferin Street
Toronto, Ontario, Canada M6K 3H6

For information about custom editions, special sales, and premium and corporate purchases,
please contact Sterling Special Sales at 800-805-5489 or specialsales@sterlingpublishing.com.

Manufactured in Canada

2 4 6 8 10 9 7 5 3 2 1

www.sterlingpublishing.com

Designed by Eleanor Kwei